The FOSSil Hunters

Written by **Cath Jones**   Illustrated by **Juanbjuan Oliver**

Chapter 1

Pearl paused outside the entrance to her new school.

"Don't worry," said Mum. "I'm sure you'll make friends really quickly."

"But what if nobody talks to me?" Pearl asked.

Mum hugged her. "You'll be fine," she whispered. "Have you got your lucky stone?"

"Yes."

"You could tell them about how Gran found it," Mum suggested.

"Maybe..." Pearl said.

"Don't forget: Gran's picking you up later. That's something to look forward to!"

Mrs Patik, the head teacher, was waiting for Pearl inside the school gates. She took her to Orange Class.

The room was full of chatter and smiling faces. Some children waved hello as she settled at her table.

"Hi, I'm Ned…" a smiling boy said.

"And I'm Mei," interrupted a girl in a bubbly voice.

Relief flooded through Pearl.

When the buzzer rang for morning play, Pearl followed them out into the playground. In her pocket, she turned over her lucky stone. The familiar ridges of the fossil were warm and reassuring.

Ned pointed at Pearl's pocket. "What you got there?" he asked.

Pearl held out her stone. "It's a fossil," she said. "My gran found it."

"A what?"

Pearl pointed at the shape of a leaf on it.

"That's millions of years old," she said. "It's a fossilised leaf."

"I saw a programme about fossils on the telly once," said Mei.

"My gran's really good at finding fossils," Pearl said proudly. "Her job's really cool. She's a fossil hunter!"

"Digging up old rocks is a weird job," Ned said.

Pearl gazed at the rock. "She hunts for old bones too…" she said.

"Bones! That's gross!" Ned said.

"Yuck!" Mei wrinkled up her nose. She waved

towards the playing field. "Want to play football?"

Pearl was glad when the buzzer finally sounded and everyone returned to class. Football had been okay but she felt sad that they didn't like her fossil.

★★★

At home time, Pearl heard Gran long before she spotted her. A rusty old Land Rover rumbled to a halt opposite the school gates. Gran jumped out in a large floppy hat and bright orange fleece.

"Gran!" yelled Pearl.

"You survived your first day!" Gran said. She gave Pearl a hug. "Fancy a trip to the beach on Saturday for a bit of fossil hunting?" she asked.

"Oh yes please!" Pearl said. A wave of happiness washed over her.

Chapter 2

When Saturday finally arrived, Pearl, Gran and Mum headed for the beach. Gran had a surprise present for Pearl.

"Your very own fossil hunting backpack," Gran said.

Pearl's heart leapt with excitement as she unzipped it. Inside was a fossil hunting kit! There was a hammer, a chisel, strong gloves, a trowel,

a brush, safety goggles, a magnifying glass, some tweezers and a book on fossils.

"Wow, thanks Gran!" said Pearl.

They set off along the beach, leaving Mum setting up camp. Armed with her fossil hunting kit, Pearl felt very important!

Gran knelt down on the sand. She crawled around looking at the rocks and turning them over.

This wasn't what Pearl had been expecting. It wasn't very exciting! "When do we start to dig and hammer?" She pointed hopefully at the cliffs.

Gran chuckled. "We won't be digging or

hammering into the cliffs. That's dangerous. We'll stay away from the bottom of the cliff too, just in case any rocks fall." Gran pointed at a pile of rocks. "They look interesting," she said.

Pearl jumped onto the pile. All the rocks looked the same to her. Suddenly, she pointed to the bottom of the pile. "Look!" she gasped. "Is that part of a fossil hidden in the sand?"

Gran brushed some of the sand away. "I think you're right! It looks like a bit of an enormous ammonite.

Well spotted!"

"What's an amm-on-ite?" Pearl asked.

"It was a creature a bit like an octopus. But it lived in a shell. You've found its fossilised shell."

Gran and Pearl worked as a team. Together, they chipped away at the outside of the rock. After an hour, they stopped for a rest. The ammonite was bigger than a car tyre!

Pearl waved her hands in the air. "Mum!" she shrieked. "Come and look. Gran and I have found an enormous fossil."

Soon, a small crowd of people had gathered to see what all the noise was about. People started to take pictures of Pearl and her enormous fossil.

Gran looked very proud. "I think you and your enormous ammonite are going to be famous!"

Chapter 3

On Monday, Pearl made another amazing discovery. There was a photograph of her with the ammonite on the front page of the local newspaper. She was famous!

Pearl cut out the picture. When she arrived at school, she spotted Ned and Mei.

"Look," she said. She showed them her newspaper cutting.

"*Local girl finds giant fossil,*" Ned read.

"Wow!"

"That's me," Pearl said proudly. "I'm a fossil

hunter, just like my gran."

Ned beckoned to the rest of the class. "Come and look. Pearl's famous!"

Soon everyone was talking about fossils. The school buzzed with excitement.

Pearl showed them photographs of her giant ammonite.

"It was so heavy that we had to leave it on the beach," she explained. "But some of Gran's friends are going to move it with special equipment. It's going to be on display at the museum," she said proudly. She showed them some smaller ammonites she'd found.

"Cool!" said Ned. "Can I be a fossil hunter too? It looks fun."

"Could we start a fossil hunting club?" Mei asked.

Pearl grinned. "That's a brilliant idea! But I think we might need some equipment. I could ask Gran what we need..."

"Great!" Ned said. "You'll be in charge, because you're a fossil expert."

Pearl felt herself blush. "I'm not really an expert," she muttered. "That's my gran."

But neither Mei nor Ned was listening.

"Clubs need badges," Mei announced.

"And a name," Ned added.

"We could be *the Fossil Hunters*," Pearl suggested.

"The Fossil Hunters," repeated Ned. "Yeah, that's a good name."

The three of them spent breaktime making badges in the shape of ammonites. Ned wrote his name on one of the badges.

"There," he said. "I'm the first member of the Fossil Hunters."

"And I'm the second," Mei said.

By the afternoon, there were more than a dozen members.

"When are we going to have our first meeting?" Ned asked.

Pearl hopped excitedly from one foot to the other. "What about lunchtime play tomorrow?" she suggested.

Everyone agreed.

Pearl couldn't wait to get home and tell Gran about the new club.

Chapter 4

When Pearl got to school the next day, there were more than twenty children waiting to join the Fossil Hunters. She could hardly believe it.

Ned waved his hand in the air. "Shhh!" he called. "Or you won't be able to hear Pearl."

At that moment, Mrs Patik appeared in the doorway. She gave Pearl an encouraging smile, before heading down the corridor.

Pearl suddenly felt nervous. She read out loud from her fossil book. Then she showed them her fossil hunting kit. "If we're really going to look for fossils, we'll need to get some more equipment like this," she said.

Mei looked thoughtful. "So we need to raise money to buy kits for the club..." she said.

Mrs Patik wandered past again. She was peering round as if searching for something. "Well if you find my missing school keys," she said with a nervous laugh. "I'm sure you could have lots of kits!"

The children looked at each other excitedly.

"It's a huge bunch of keys. Lost this morning," Mrs Patik added as she disappeared back down the corridor.

"The Fossil Hunters' first outing!" Pearl said.

The children raced off round the school to hunt for the keys. After half an hour, they had only found a few tiny stones.

"The keys could be anywhere," Ned moaned. He was very hot, and a bit fed up!

"We need to look in the right kind of places," Pearl said. "It's just like fossil hunting."

Mei agreed. "Where does Mrs Patik usually go?"

"She was standing by the school gates this morning," Pearl said.

"Shall we start looking there?" Ned asked.

The children crawled through the long grass near the gates, hunting under leaves and branches.

They were just about to give up, when Pearl

spotted something sparkling by the litter bin.

"The keys!" she yelled.

The huge bunch of keys was almost hidden by

an empty crisp packet that had fallen out of

the bin.

The children cheered and whooped.

"The Fossil Hunters' first find!" Ned said. He grinned.

"Let's go and find Mrs Patik," Pearl said.

Chapter 5

The children gathered in front of the school reception desk.

"Hello, Mrs Wood," Pearl said.

The school secretary smiled. "Hello, Pearl. I saw you in the paper! You're famous!"

Pearl grinned. Mrs Wood looked questioningly at the children. "What have you all been up to?" she asked. "You look very pleased with yourselves."

Pearl waved at all the children. "This is the Fossil Hunters club..."

"We found something!" interrupted Ned.

Pearl held up the bunch of keys.

Mrs Wood stared at them with wide, shocked eyes. "Those aren't fossils!" she gasped.

"Mrs Wood? Are you okay?" Pearl asked.

Mrs Wood nodded. A smile spread across her face. She stood up and shouted at the top of her voice, "The keys! They've found them!"

She leapt out of her chair and raced off towards the headteacher's office.

A few moments later, a door slammed. There was the sound of footsteps running down the stairs and Mrs Patik appeared.

"Amazing! You found my missing keys!" She laughed happily.

Pearl suddenly didn't know what to say. She just grinned.

"We were going to have to change all the locks in the whole school. You've saved us so many problems." She beamed at the children.

Ned pointed at his ammonite-shaped badge. "The Fossil Hunters found them," he said.

"Of course, Pearl's new club!" Mrs Patik said with a thoughtful expression. Then she smiled. "Kits! Your new club needs fossil hunting equipment. That's right, isn't it?"

Pearl nodded and Mei grinned.

Mrs Patik handed them a piece of paper.

"Make me a list of what the Fossil Hunters need.

If we make this an official school club, we can

order you everything you need."

Chapter 6

The Fossil Hunters club had their first official trip the next weekend. They went to the beach with Pearl's gran. Each member had their own backpack full of kit. Mrs Patik had kept her promise!

"Did you know someone once found a dinosaur on this beach?" Gran said.

"A dinosaur!" Pearl exclaimed.

"Could there be more hidden dinosaurs?" Ned asked hopefully.

Gran laughed. "Well, if we look really hard and are very lucky, we might find a dinosaur *footprint*."

"Ooh! That sounds cool," Mei said.

Gran tapped her phone and held up a picture. "I found this fossilised footprint last year."

"Awesome!" said Mei.

"I want to find a dinosaur!" Ned said in a loud voice.

"ROAR!" Pearl shouted and she chased Ned and Mei until they all collapsed laughing onto the sand.

"Close your eyes," she panted. "Imagine this beach with dinosaurs walking around."

Ned giggled. "Imagine going for a swim and meeting a dinosaur!"

"Or dinosaurs stamping on all your sandcastles!" Mei added.

"We're going back in time," Gran interrupted in a whisper. "One hundred and twenty-five million years ago, this beach would have been swampy and wet. There were all sorts of creatures living here, like crocodiles!"

Pearl sat up. "Come on, let's start looking for fossils. Maybe we'll find a fossilised crocodile tooth!" she said. She got everyone to bend down and start turning over the rocks on the ground.

After a few minutes, Mei suddenly gasped. "Look!" she exclaimed and held up a rock shaped like a tiny coiled up shell.

At the same moment, Ned let out an excited whoop. "I've got a fossil too!" he yelled.

Pearl glowed with pride. It was lovely that her new friends were enjoying fossil hunting so much! She was sure the Fossil Hunters club was going to be a huge hit!

Discussion Points

1. Why was Pearl nervous about her new school in the beginning?

2. Where did Pearl and Gran find the giant ammonite?

a) In the mountains

b) At the beach

c) Underwater

3. What was your favourite part of the story?

4. What has Mrs Patik, the headteacher, lost in the story?

FOSSIL HUNTERS CLUB

5. Why do you think the Fossil Hunters club needs equipment?

6. Who was your favourite character and why?

7. There were moments in the story when Pearl has to be **confident**. How does she find her confidence?

8. What do you think happens after the end of the story?

Book Bands for Guided Reading

The Institute of Education book banding system is a scale of colours that reflects the various levels of reading difficulty. The bands are assigned by taking into account the content, the language style, the layout and phonics. Word, phrase and sentence level work is also taken into consideration.

The Maverick Readers Scheme is a bright, attractive range of books covering the pink to grey bands. All of these books have been book banded for guided reading to the industry standard and edited by a leading educational consultant.

To view the whole Maverick Readers scheme, visit our website at
www.maverickearlyreaders.com

Or scan the QR code to view our scheme instantly!

Maverick Chapter Readers
(From Lime to Grey Band)